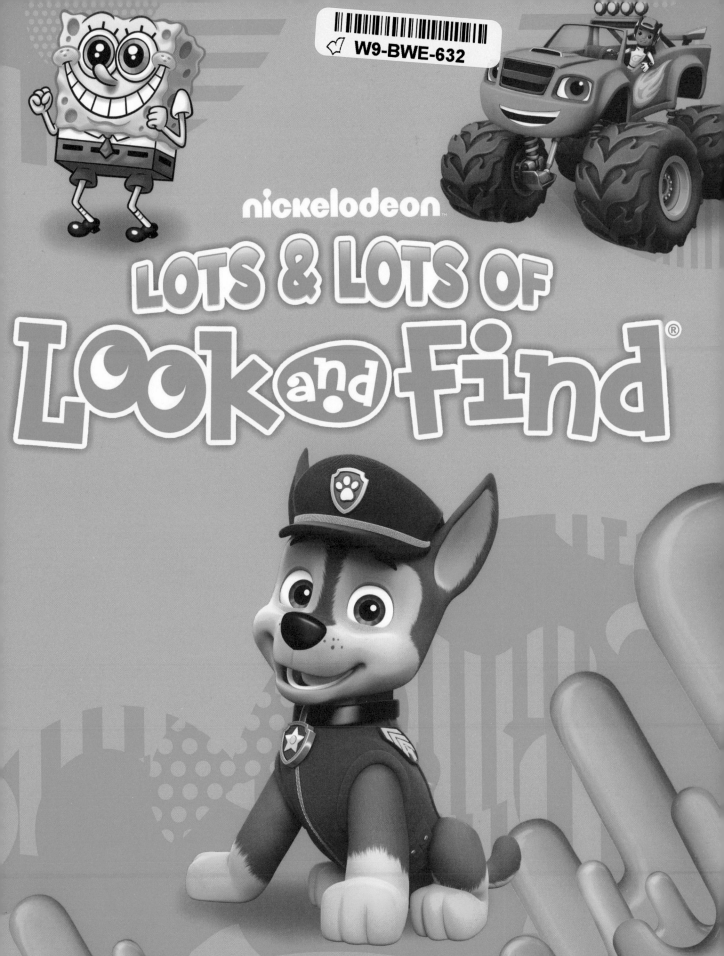

nickelodeon™

LOTS & LOTS OF
Look and Find®

pi kids®

phoenix international publications, inc.

Look and Find

Look at the items in the colored border. Then, search for those items in the picture. When you've found them all, check the lower right corner of the page for another challenge!

What's Different?

When you see a pair of pictures, try to find what's different. There are 10 differences between each pair. Can you spot them all?

"Pups away to solve some puzzles!"

"I'm fired up to look and find!"

Look and Find

PAW Patrol is on a roll! Ryder and the pups are heading out of the Lookout to help around Adventure Bay. Can you find each pup?

Adventure Bay is a colorful place to play! Look out for things in each of these colors:

Look and Find

Ready, set, get wet! Zuma races to Cap'n Turbot's boat to patch a leak. Rocky stays behind—and he stays nice and dry! Find these other animals in the sand, sea, or sky:

Two things that go together are a pair. Comb the beach and find these six pairs of seashells:

Look and Find

Farmer Yumi needs a helping hand—or paw—at harvest time. Rubble digs in with his bulldozer. Help find these farm signs:

Farmer Yumi knows she can always count on PAW Patrol. Can you count these things?

1 pitchfork 5 baskets 8 chicks
2 trucks 6 pups 10 pumpkins

Look and Find

Buckle up! It's time for an Adventure Bay road race. When Alex needs help getting his trike back on the road, Chase is on the case! Find these vehicles behind Chase's roadblock:

Let's roll! Search the race scene for these signs:

STOP CAUTION YIELD

Look and Find

Uh-oh! Mayor Goodway can't find Chickaletta anywhere! Marshall is all fired up! He climbs his ladder to search the trees. Can you help find Chickaletta and these other birds, too?

Skye and fly rhyme. Sniff around City Hall and find these other things that rhyme:

- rock and clock
- shell and bell
- tree and bee
- sign and nine (9)
- wheel and peel
- pots and spots

Look and Find

Adventure Bay Snow Day is about to begin! But Jake is stuck on a snowy mountain ledge. Ice or snow, Everest is ready to go! While she uses her pup pack to save the day, find these tools on the mountain:

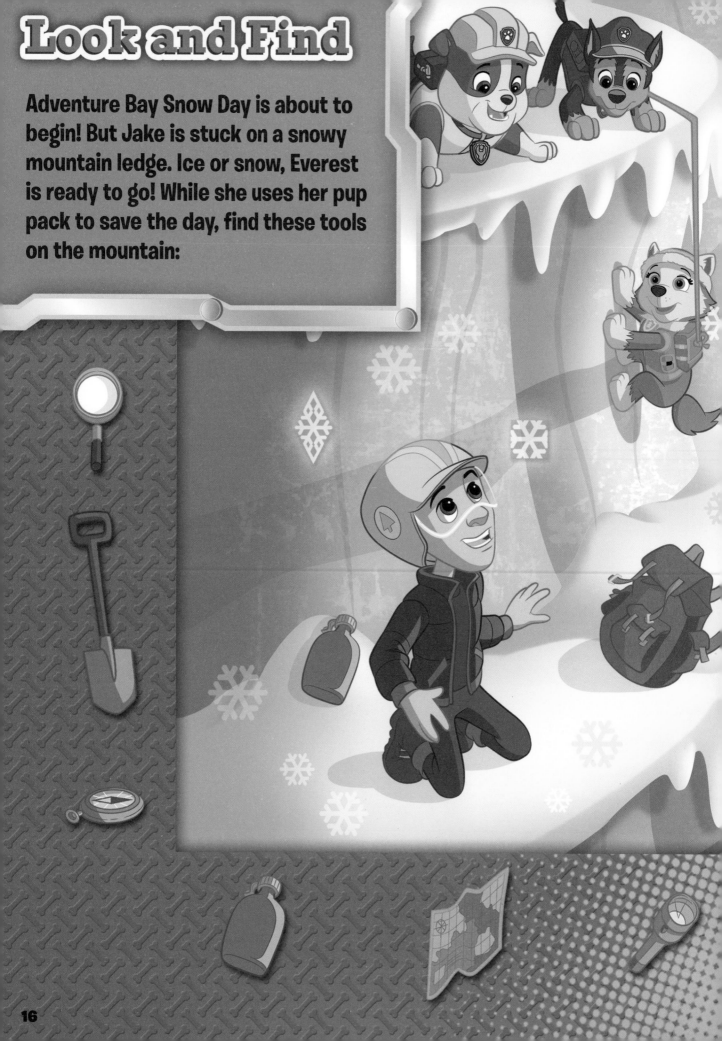

Snow way! Scan the mountain for snowflakes in these PAWsome shapes:

Look and Find

It's a pup-tastic party at Mr. Porter's! Skye's gotta fly, while Chase opens up the delivery truck to drop off more gifts and PAWsome decorations. Search the tables for these treats:

Spec

DELIVERY

This pup's gotta fly to make cake and pie! Can you help find these ingredients?

19

Look and Find

Who wants to play? The pups love to hit the Pup Park with Ryder. Run, ride, skate, and slide along with the PAW Patrol as you find these playground things:

When the pups save the day, Ryder gives them pup treats to celebrate a job well done. Patrol the Pup Park and find 10 pup treats.

What's Different?

22

Can you help find 10 differences in the pictures?

Answers on page 30

What's Different?

The pups spend a PAWsitively relaxing day at the beach!

What's Different?

PAW Patrol is on a roll, heading out on a new mission!

What's Different?

Ahoy! The pups are on a pirate adventure!

Take out your spyglass and spot
10 differences between the pirate
pictures.

What's Different?

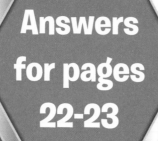

Answers for pages 22-23

Answers for pages 24-25

Answers for pages 26-27

Answers for pages 28-29

SHIMMER and Shine

Boom Zahramay!

Shimmer and Shine—let's look and find!

Puzzles turn out better when we work together!

33

Look and Find

Welcome to Zahramay Falls, home of twin genies-in-training, Shimmer and Shine. Look for these landmarks as Shimmer and Shine soar high above:

Swoosh through the clouds and find these sky-high items:

Look and Find

When Shimmer and Shine are looking for the best bargains in Zahramay Falls, they head to the Azar Bazaar. Help spot these treats and trinkets:

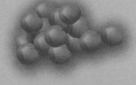

Stroll through the market and help Shimmer and Shine find all the things on their list:

Look and Find

When the temperature rises, Shimmer and Shine spend a magical day at Bela Beach. Stroll along the shore and locate these seaside things:

Make a splash at Bela Beach as you search for these sandy treasures:

Look and Find

Shimmer and Shine grant three wishes a day to their best friend Leah. Today, the friends are baking cupcakes! Search for these things in Leah's kitchen:

Scan Leah's kitchen for these sweet treats:

Look and Find

Leah's neighbor Zac is putting on a magic show, so Leah's secret genies need to do a little magic of their own and disappear! Look for Shimmer and Shine and these other magical things:

Zac reached into his hat and got more bunnies than he bargained for! Can you find these?

Look and Find

When Leah wishes for a tree house, Shimmer and Shine turn her house into a tree! Oopsie! Find some critters lurking in this homey habitat:

Roam around Leah's living room and find these blooming flowers:

Look and Find

Shimmer, Shine, and Leah turn on their favorite music and have a genie-rific dance party! Help find these colorful dresses to add sparkle to their step:

Look around Leah's bedroom for these glittery dance-party costume accessories:

Look and Find

Back in Zahramay Falls, Shimmer, Shine, Tala, and Nahal play hide-and-seek before snuggling on the sofa. Look around the living room and find what else is hiding:

Shimmer and Shine are ready to get cozy!
Can you find these comfy things?

What's Different?

Can you spot 10 differences in the scenes?

Answers on page 58

What's Different?

Tala is Shimmer's playful monkey, and Nahal is Shine's cuddly tiger.

Can you track down 10 differences in the playful pet pictures?

Answers on page 58

What's Different?

Shimmer and Shine are on their way to grant Leah's wishes!

**Check for 10 differences in
the soaring scenes.**

Answers on page 59

What's Different?

Shimmer and Shine live in a world of magic.

Answers on page 59

What's Different?

Answers
for pages
50-51

Answers
for pages
52-53

Answers
for pages
54-55

Answers
for pages
56-57

Look and Find

Blaze and his best friend AJ live in Axle City, an awesome place filled with races, chases, and mighty Monster Machines! Search this city scene for Blaze and his pals:

Look around Axle City to see what you can find:

above the Monster Dome

in front of the Monster Dome

below the sun

behind Gabby

next to Crusher

on Starla's head

Look and Find

At Axle City Garage and Truck Wash, no job is too tough for Gabby! She's a mechanic with serious know-how. Look around the garage for her helpful hand tools:

Search for these other tools around the Axle City garage:

Look and Find

Beep-beep! Smash! Thud! Blaze and Zeg are using FORCE to help knock things over at a busy construction site. Look for their construction vehicle friends:

Cruise around the construction site and find these shapes:

▲ triangle

● oval

◆ diamond

■ square

▬ rectangle

● circle

67

Look and Find

Blaze, Darington, Crusher, and Pickle head to the Badlands for a Team Truck Challenge race. As the Monster Machines ACCELERATE around the racecourse, can you find two flags of each color?

Drive through the Badlands to find things that rhyme with these words:

tree (bee)   maze (Blaze)   steel (wheel)

zoom (fume)   fun (sun)   car (star)

Look and Find

Roar! It's time to play hide-and-seek in Stripes' jungle home! Can you find Stripes, Blaze, and these other friends who are hiding?

Journey through the jungle to find and count these things:

1 slide   3 rocks   5 shrubs

2 clouds   4 flowers   6 palm trees

Look and Find

Anchors aweigh! Sometimes the Monster Machines race on water, too! As Blaze and AJ sail past Crusher and Pickle, help them look for these ocean-themed things:

Water begins with **w**. Sail the ocean and find these other things that also begin with the letter **w**:

waves   wind   wing

whale   wheel   window

Look and Find

Everyone in Axle City has gathered to watch Blaze and Crusher compete at the Monster Dome. Blaze is in it to win it. As he zooms towards the finish line, can you find these excited cars in the crowd?

Blaze around the Monster Dome and find these car parts:

headlights　　　windshield　　　taillights
bumper　　　tire　　　hood

What's Different?

Ta-da! It's another almost-perfect landing for Darington!

Spot 10 differences as Darington defies gravity.

Answers on page 84

What's Different?

Let's Blaaaze! All the Monster Machines are ready to roll!

Can you spot 10 differences in the scenes?

Answers on page 84

What's Different?

What's Different?

Yeehaw! Starla and Blaze are showing off their skills.

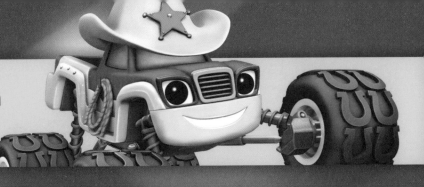

What's Different?

Answers for pages 76-77

Answers for pages 78-79

Answers for pages 80-81

Answers for pages 82-83

Let's wrangle some riddles, y'all!

Let's get to the Bikini Bottom of these puzzles!

I'm ready,
I'm ready,
I'm ready!

Look and Find

SpongeBob SquarePants needs to do his spring cleaning. When he opens his closet to find his springs, everything crashes down on his spongy head. Look through the mess for this silly stuff:

Find these things to help SpongeBob clean up this mess:

a broom
a bucket
soap on a rope

a red towel
fish-shaped scrub brush
Swiss Army bubble wand

Look and Find

The junk from SpongeBob's closet knocked him silly. He wakes up in Welcome Land! While SpongeBob is trying to make some sense of his senses, find all of these super-happy characters:

Look around Welcome Land for these welcoming things:

welcome mat
welcome wagon
fruit cake
house plant
welcome wheel of cheese
welcome basket

Look and Find

SpongeBob loves a parade! He is thrilled to cruise down Main Street on the float of honor. Look around the parade route to find all this seaworthy silliness:

March around the Welcome Land parade to find these yummy treats:

a porcupine pie

cotton candy

caramel apple

marshmallows on a stick

a seashell salad

a licorice lasso

Look and Find

The Mayor of Welcome Land escorts SpongeBob to his Welcome Land home. SpongeBob has never seen such sandtastic stuff! Look around his new home and see what he sees:

Take another look and find these things that remind Spongebob of Bikini Bottom:

a pineapple
a tree dome
a jellyfishing net

employee of the month plaque
a can of snail food
Squidward's clarinet

Look and Find

All of this excitement in Welcome Land has given SpongeBob an unsinkable hunger. Look around this salty spread to find these foods SpongeBob can't wait to try:

Sit down at the big dinner party and find these noisemakers:

a bulb horn

a cowbell

a triangle

a drum

a whistle

a duck

Look and Find

The well-meaning characters of Welcome Land bring things to remind SpongeBob of home. But everything is just a little different. See if you can find what is wrong before SpongeBob does:

SPONGEBOB SQUAREHAT

Scan the homesick scene to find these mixed-up things:

scrambled eggs   milkshake

jigsaw puzzle   deck of cards

scrambled words   a juggler

Look and Find

SpongeBob really misses Bikini Bottom. To get back home, he runs right into a mailbox to un-bump his head! See if you can find the nautical nonsense floating around SpongeBob's dizzy noggin:

Swirl around SpongeBob's spinning head to find these lumpy things:

a camel

a bowl of oatmeal

a gravy boat

a pillow

a stack of pancakes

an argyle sock

Look and Find

When SpongeBob wakes up, Patrick welcomes him home, but SpongeBob doesn't want to hear the word "welcome" ever again. Find these things that Patrick used to wake up SpongeBob:

Roll through Patrick's rock house to find these other things that "rock":

rock star

rocking chair

a rock and roll

rock hammer

rocking horse

rocket

103

What's Different?

104

Answers on page 112

What's Different?

These best pals always give each other a salty smile!

These best pals always give each other a salty smile!

Answers on page 112

What's Different?

Ta-daa! The perfect Krabby Patty... brought to you by SpongeBob!

What's Different?

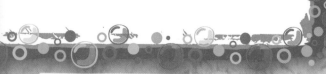

Patrick sure has a lot of old junk!

Can you spot 10 differences between the untidy pictures?

Answers on page 113

What's Different?

Answers for pages
104-105

Answers for pages
106-107

¡Vámonos!
Let's look
and find!

Look and Find

Dora is searching for these colorful things in the Crystal Kingdom. Will you help?

DORA

01

¿Dónde están los cristales? **Will you help find all the different colored crystals?**

yellow	blue
red	green
purple	white

Look and Find

Hooray! Today is Dora's ballet recital! Will you help her find these things she needs to put on a dance show? *¡Muy bien!*

DORA

01

Do you see
these shapes
that are hiding
at the recital?

Look and Find

Dora needs to get King Unicornio to his castle! Can you find all these creatures from the Enchanted Forest along the way?

The Enchanted Forest has so many animal friends!
Do you see these animal friends? *¡Los animales!*

skunk   mouse

raccoon   owl

squirrel   rabbit

Look and Find

Tico's *mami* is a brave firefighter. Can you find these items that help her keep everyone safe?

DORA

01

Lots of things that firefighters use are red.
Can you find these other red items before Swiper
swipes them?

red cardinal   red sports car
red traffic light   red apple
red stop sign   red playground ball

Look and Find

Tico is scoring the winning goal! Can you find all the different soccer balls?

WE ♥

DORA 01

Each player gets a different number. Can you spot these numbers on the players' uniforms?

6	5	7	2
9	1	10	8
4	3	11	

Look and Find

Dora and Boots are stargazing, and look—Isa is in a rocket ship! What else can Dora and Boots see when they look in the telescope?

DORA

01 ★

Rocket through the sky and find these shapes hidden in the stars:

- circle
- triangle
- square
- rectangle
- oval
- diamond

127

Look and Find

Diego saves animals high and low!
Search this mountaintop for all of
these mountain animals:

DORA 01

Can you help find these mountain animals and this mountain animal rescue gear?

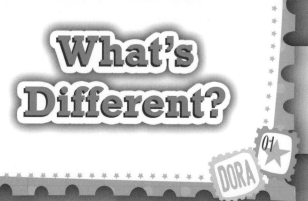

What's Different?

¡Buenos días! Good morning!
Dora is getting ready for the day.

Answers on page 138

What's Different?

DORA 01

Dora and Mariana are busy cleaning up the Mermaid Kingdom!

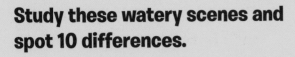

Answers on page 138

What's Different?

Dora and her friends are wearing silly hats!

134

Can you find 10 differences between the scenes? *¡Excelente!*

Answers on page 139

What's Different?

Diego's family works together at the Animal Rescue Center.

Help out by spotting 10 differences between the pictures!

Answers on page 139

What's Different?

DORA 01

Answers
for pages
130-131

Answers
for pages
132-133

TEAM UMIZOOMI™

Umifriend, we need your Look and Find help!

It's time for action!

Look and Find

Milli, Geo, and Bot are ready for a Rolling Toy Parade. Can you find them and the missing pieces of the rolling lion?

142

Roll through the Toy Parade and help us find these things that go:

143

Look and Find

Can you spot these floating things as Team Umizoomi fixes the aquarium?

Splash around the aquarium and look for these super underwater shapes:

- triangle
- half circle
- diamond
- circle
- oval
- star

Look and Find

The toy store is full of great toys! Can you help Milli, Geo, and Bot spot these favorites?

Find Sparkle Pup at the toy store and take a look at the price tag. Then find 5 coins that add up to the right price!

Look and Find

It's a beautiful day at the Umi City Zoo! Help Team Umizoomi find these baby animals:

Swing through the zoo and find these animal parents:

Look and Find

Team Umizoomi, it's time for action! Will you help find this fire rescue gear?

Two things that go together make a pair. See if you can spot these pairs around the fire station:

- boots
- traffic cones
- fire hats
- fire extinguishers

Look and Find

Team Umizoomi heads to the Toy Train Show! Help them find a ticket along with these Wild West items:

Chug past the Wild West Toy Train Show and try to spot trains in these colors:

- red
- orange
- yellow
- green
- blue
- purple

Look and Find

Milli, Geo, and Bot take to the sky at the Kite Festival! Can you help them find these flying things?

Fly around the Kite Festival and spot these pieces of the dragon kite from Bot's Belly, Belly, Bellyscreen!

What's Different?

Bot is juggling three balls in Umi City!

Answers on page 164

What's Different?

Answers on page 164

What's Different?

It's the perfect day for ice cream!

200

200

300

150

200

350

12

Search for 10 differences in these sweet pictures.

Answers on
page 165

What's Different?

We are playing hide-and-seek with our toys!

**Answers on
page 165**

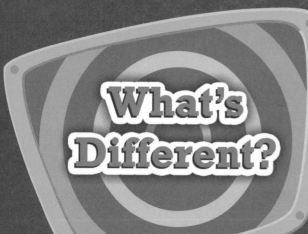

What's Different?

Answers
for pages
156-157

Answers
for pages
158-159

**Answers
for pages
160-161**

**Answers
for pages
162-163**

BUBBLE GUPPIES ™

Would you like to play with us?

Awesome!

Look and Find

Time for school! Find these things in the Bubble Guppies' classroom:

Cruise around the classroom to find these shapes:

circle

oval

star

heart

triangle

rectangle

Look and Find

Arr, matey! The Bubble Guppies are pirates! Help them find these pirate things at the beach:

Can you figure out these pirate puzzlers?
Who is closer to the:

treasure chest: Goby or Deema?   **treasure map:** Molly or Oona?
rowboat: Oona or Mr. Grouper?   **pirate:** Gil or Mr. Grouper?
spyglass: Gil or Goby?   **anchor:** Deema or Nonny?

Look and Find

The Bubble Guppies are on a swim-sational camping trip. Do you see these things around the campsite?

Hike around the campsite to count these things in the moonlight:

1 moon
2 owls
3 tents
4 hats
5 stars
6 marshmallows

Look and Find

The Bubble Guppies are on a fin-tastic field trip to the farm. Will you find these farm things?

Mosey around the farm to look for these animals.
What sounds do they make?

rooster   duck
cow   horse
pig   sheep

Look and Find

Time to go shopping with the Bubble Guppies! Look for these things at the supermarket:

Check it out! Can you find these fruit and vegetable pairs at the supermarket?

pair of apples
pair of banana bunches
pair of pears

pair of carrots
pair of peppers
pair of watermelons

Look and Find

Get ready to rock! Search the stage for these instruments:

Rock around the stage and find bandannas in these colors:

red

blue

green

pink

purple

orange

Look and Find

Boo! Find these things inside the Bubble Guppies' haunted house:

Haunted begins with the letter **h**. Sneak through the **h**aunted **h**ouse to find more things that begin with the letter **h**:

hair   **h**ouse

hand   **h**orn

heart   **h**at

What's Different?

Spot 10 differences in the storefront scenes.

Answers on page 190

What's Different?

Gil floats past speedy Mrs. Peekytoe in search of pet food!

What's Different?

Check out the Bubble Guppies in the checkout line at the undersea supermarket

Answers on page 191

What's Different?

See if you can spot 10 differences.

Answers on page 191

What's Different?

Answers
for pages
182-183

Answers
for pages
184-185

190

**Answers
for pages
186-187**

**Answers
for pages
188-189**

The puzzles turned out great!

PAWsitively awesome!

High tire!